WHERE'S SANTA?

Tony Tallarico

Kidsbooks®

Here we are at Santa's World Headquarters at the North Pole.

SEARCH FOR SANTA AT HIS HEADQUARTERS AND...

- ☐ Balls (3)
- ☐ Banana peel
- ☐ Candy canes (4)
- ☐ Dogs (2)
- ☐ Drummer
- ☐ Envelope
- ☐ Gingerbread house
- ☐ Goose
- ☐ Hammock
- ☐ Hearts (2)
- ☐ Igloo
- ☐ Jack-in-the-box
- ☐ Kite
- ☐ Lips
- ☐ Partridge in a pear tree
- ☐ Pick
- ☐ Pillow
- ☐ Rabbit
- ☐ Sandwich
- ☐ Skier
- ☐ Sleeping tree
- ☐ Sleigh
- ☐ Snowballs (3)
- ☐ Snow shovels (2)
- ☐ Snow women (2)
- ☐ Snowmen (2)
- ☐ Starts (4)
- ☐ Stocking
- ☐ Sunglasses
- ☐ Tepee
- ☐ Tricycle
- ☐ Wreaths (2)

Santa's elves work very hard to make sure the toys are ready by Christmas Eve.

SEARCH FOR SANTA IN THE ELVES' WORKSHOP AND...

- ☐ Baseball
- ☐ Boat
- ☐ Brushes (2)
- ☐ Coffeepot
- ☐ Crayons (2)
- ☐ Dogs (2)
- ☐ Ducks (2)
- ☐ Fire truck
- ☐ Football
- ☐ Hammers (2)
- ☐ Helicopter
- ☐ Kite
- ☐ Knife
- ☐ Mouse
- ☐ Paddle
- ☐ Piggy bank
- ☐ Pinocchio
- ☐ Robot
- ☐ Saw
- ☐ Scissors
- ☐ Screwdriver
- ☐ Star
- ☐ Teddy bear
- ☐ Telescope
- ☐ Toy soldier
- ☐ Train engines (4)
- ☐ Triangle
- ☐ Ventriloquist
- ☐ Yo-yo

Santa decided to do this Christmas shopping in town this year. He may never try this again!

SEARCH FOR SANTA IN TOWN AND...

- ☐ Bat
- ☐ Bird
- ☐ Candle
- ☐ Cats (2)
- ☐ Dog
- ☐ Drum
- ☐ Fishing pole
- ☐ Football
- ☐ Ice-cream cone
- ☐ Paper airplanes
- ☐ Pig
- ☐ Pizza
- ☐ Rabbit
- ☐ Radio
- ☐ Roller skates
- ☐ Scrooge
- ☐ Shark
- ☐ Ship
- ☐ Shovel
- ☐ Sled
- ☐ Snowmen (3)
- ☐ Star
- ☐ Stocking
- ☐ Sword
- ☐ Target
- ☐ Tepee
- ☐ Toast
- ☐ Train engine
- ☐ Turtle
- ☐ Wreaths (8)

It's the morning of December 24th, and the elves are packing the sleigh. Can it take off with all the weight?

SEARCH FOR SANTA AT THE SLEIGH LOADING AND...

- ☐ Balloon
- ☐ Birdhouse
- ☐ Blimp
- ☐ Boat
- ☐ Camera
- ☐ Car
- ☐ Crayons (3)
- ☐ Flashlight
- ☐ Giraffe
- ☐ Guitar
- ☐ Hammer
- ☐ Hockey stick
- ☐ Horseshoe
- ☐ Kite
- ☐ License plate
- ☐ Mask
- ☐ Mechanic
- ☐ Needle
- ☐ Paintbrush
- ☐ Pencils (2)
- ☐ Pizza
- ☐ Rocking chair
- ☐ Sailboat
- ☐ Seal
- ☐ Skates
- ☐ Stockings (2)
- ☐ Tent
- ☐ Thread
- ☐ Train engine
- ☐ Tricycle
- ☐ Trucks (3)
- ☐ Windmill

Christmas Eve. Time to deliver the presents. Wait—something is very wrong! The sleigh has taken off and Santa's not on it!

SEARCH FOR SANTA ON CHRISTMAS EVE AND...

- ☐ Balloons (2)
- ☐ Barrel
- ☐ Bird
- ☐ Blocks
- ☐ Candy canes (2)
- ☐ Chimneys (12)
- ☐ Dog
- ☐ Drum
- ☐ Eskimo
- ☐ Happy stars (2)
- ☐ Igloo
- ☐ Ladder
- ☐ Mrs. Claus
- ☐ Robot
- ☐ Sherlock Elf
- ☐ Snow woman
- ☐ Snowman
- ☐ Teddy bear
- ☐ Telephones (2)
- ☐ Telescopes (3)
- ☐ Television
- ☐ Tent
- ☐ Truck
- ☐ TV antennas (2)
- ☐ Yo-yo

Down the chimney he goes. But someone forgot to tell the family pet that Santa was coming!

SEARCH FOR SANTA AT HOUSE NUMBER 26 AND...

- ☐ Balloons (15)
- ☐ Bats (2)
- ☐ Bird
- ☐ Broom
- ☐ Burned out lights (6)
- ☐ Cactus
- ☐ Candles (2)
- ☐ Candy canes (2)
- ☐ Cat with a horn
- ☐ Cat in a hat
- ☐ Chairs (2)
- ☐ Christmas ornaments (4)
- ☐ Ducks (2)
- ☐ Elephant
- ☐ Fish
- ☐ Football
- ☐ Footprints
- ☐ Ghost
- ☐ Heart
- ☐ Jack-o'-lantern
- ☐ Kite
- ☐ Mitten
- ☐ Pencils (3)
- ☐ Mouse
- ☐ Pie
- ☐ Scarves (2)
- ☐ Stockings (3)
- ☐ Star
- ☐ Thermometer
- ☐ Traffic ticket
- ☐ Train engine
- ☐ Trash can
- ☐ Truck
- ☐ Trunks (2)
- ☐ Turtle
- ☐ Wreaths (4)

That night Santa visits homes all over the world, bringing Christmas cheer to all!

SEARCH FOR SANTA DELIVERING PRESENTS AND...

- [ ] Airplane
- [ ] Arrows (3)
- [ ] Bat
- [ ] Book
- [ ] Burned out lights (6)
- [ ] Candles (2)
- [ ] Doll
- [ ] Drum
- [ ] Fake Santas (7)
- [ ] Football helmet
- [ ] Ghosts (2)
- [ ] Heart
- [ ] Ice-cream cone
- [ ] Kite
- [ ] Necktie
- [ ] Roller skate
- [ ] Scarf
- [ ] Sleigh
- [ ] Spotlight
- [ ] Stars (3)
- [ ] Teddy bear
- [ ] Thermometer
- [ ] Top hat
- [ ] Train engine
- [ ] TV antenna
- [ ] Wooden soldier
- [ ] Wreaths (10)

Santa is homeward bound... or is he? Can he find his way back to the North Pole?

SEARCH FOR SANTA ON EARTH AND IN SPACE AND...

- ☐ Balloons (2)
- ☐ Banana peel
- ☐ Beam
- ☐ Cactus
- ☐ Camera
- ☐ Elephant head
- ☐ Eyeglasses
- ☐ Fish (3)
- ☐ Hamburger
- ☐ Hot dog
- ☐ Igloo
- ☐ Jet sleigh
- ☐ Kite
- ☐ Magnifying glass
- ☐ Movie star
- ☐ Paper airplane
- ☐ Periscope
- ☐ Pie
- ☐ Pizza
- ☐ Rabbit
- ☐ Sherlock Holmes
- ☐ Snowmen (2)
- ☐ Super hero
- ☐ Tall elves (2)
- ☐ Telescope
- ☐ Train engine
- ☐ Unicorn

Home at last. Santa sure has a neat way of getting on and off his sleigh.

SEARCH FOR SANTA
BACK AT THE
NORTH POLE AND...

- [ ] Anteater
- [ ] Bats (2)
- [ ] Buffalo
- [ ] Camel
- [ ] Cheese
- [ ] Cow
- [ ] Dog
- [ ] Frog
- [ ] Flamingo
- [ ] Fox
- [ ] Kangaroo
- [ ] Kites (2)
- [ ] Ladder
- [ ] Mouse
- [ ] Owl
- [ ] Piggy bank
- [ ] Porpoise
- [ ] Rhinoceros
- [ ] Scarf
- [ ] Seal
- [ ] Star
- [ ] Toy soldier
- [ ] Umbrella
- [ ] Walruses (2)
- [ ] Wreath

The elves have asked Santa to attend a meeting. He doesn't know why, but he soon gets quite a surprise

SEARCH FOR SANTA AT THE SURPRISE PARTY AND...

- [ ] Balloon
- [ ] Bearded elf
- [ ] Clothesline
- [ ] Clown
- [ ] Cookies
- [ ] Elephants
- [ ] Envelope
- [ ] Fish
- [ ] Giraffe
- [ ] Hammer
- [ ] Heart
- [ ] Ice-cream cone
- [ ] Kiddie pool
- [ ] Mrs. Claus
- [ ] Reindeer
- [ ] Robot
- [ ] Saw
- [ ] Scooter
- [ ] Sir Prize
- [ ] Star
- [ ] Stocking
- [ ] TV camera
- [ ] Toy duck
- [ ] Wagon

On the twelfth day of Christmas my true love gave to me:

- ☐ **12 Drummers Drumming**
- ☐ **11 Pipers Piping**
- ☐ **10 Lords-a-leaping**
- ☐ **9 Ladies Dancing**
- ☐ **8 Maids-a-Milking**
- ☐ **7 Swans-a-Swimming**
- ☐ **6 Geese-a-Laying**

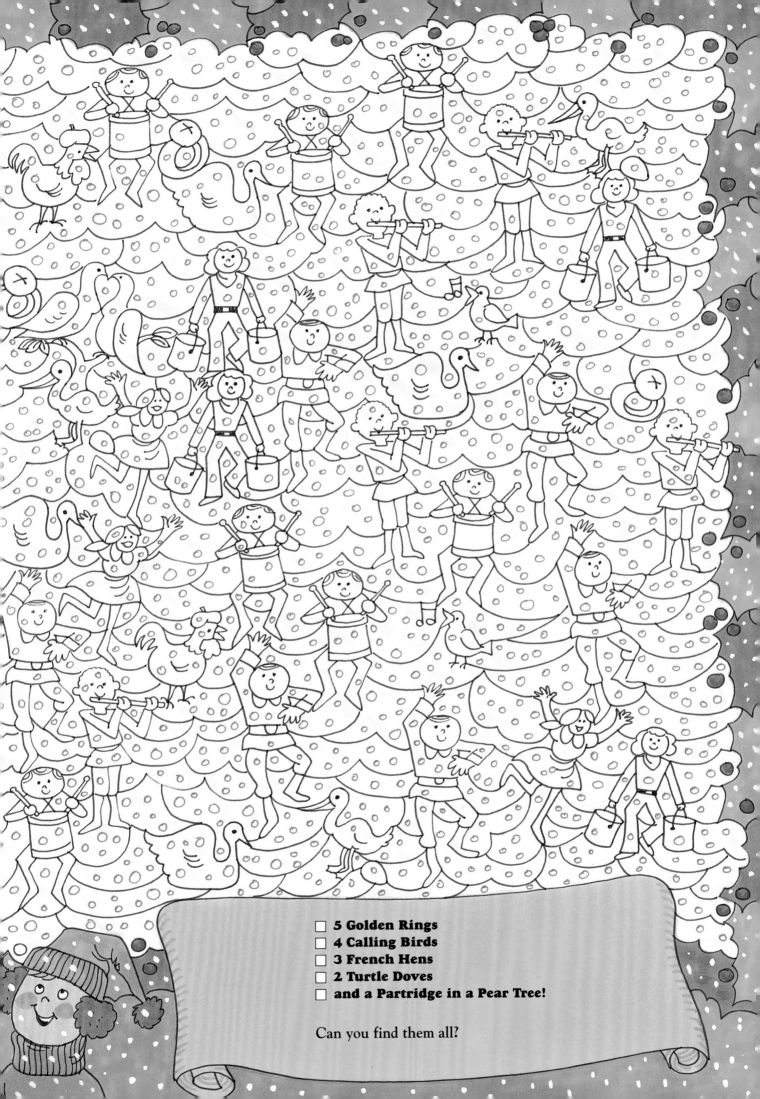

□ 5 Golden Rings
□ 4 Calling Birds
□ 3 French Hens
□ 2 Turtle Doves
□ and a Partridge in a Pear Tree!

Can you find them all?

Fee Fi
Fo Fun

The elves made so many gifts this year that they're running out of places in which to store them.

SEARCH FOR FEE, FI, FO, AND FUN AT THE GIFT STORAGE CENTER AND...

- [ ] Baseball bat
- [ ] Bell
- [ ] Book
- [ ] Bowling ball
- [ ] Candy canes (3)
- [ ] Clown
- [ ] Duck
- [ ] Earmuffs (2 pairs)
- [ ] Elves with beards (3)
- [ ] Empty warehouse
- [ ] Fishing pole
- [ ] Flower
- [ ] Footballs (2)
- [ ] Horse
- [ ] Igloo
- [ ] Jack-in-the-box
- [ ] Kite
- [ ] Lion
- [ ] Mouse
- [ ] Rabbits (2)
- [ ] Robot
- [ ] Santa Claus
- [ ] Scarecrow
- [ ] Scarves (8)
- [ ] Shoemaker
- [ ] Skier
- [ ] Snake
- [ ] Telescopes (2)
- [ ] Thermometer
- [ ] Toy elephants (3)
- [ ] Train engine
- [ ] Turtle
- [ ] Unicorn
- [ ] Watch

Fee Fi Fo Fun

This is the place where all those fancy bows and ribbons are made.

SEARCH FOR FEE, FI, FO, AND FUN AT THE BIG BOW WORKS AND...

- [ ] Airplane
- [ ] Balloon
- [ ] Bell
- [ ] Bunny
- [ ] Cat
- [ ] Clown
- [ ] Cow
- [ ] Crayon
- [ ] Cup
- [ ] Dog
- [ ] Elephant
- [ ] Flying bat
- [ ] Garden hose
- [ ] Ghost
- [ ] Globe
- [ ] Guitar
- [ ] Hot dog
- [ ] Jack-o'-lantern
- [ ] Jack-in-the-box
- [ ] Jump rope
- [ ] Lollipops (3)
- [ ] Oilcan
- [ ] Package
- [ ] Paint bucket
- [ ] Panda
- [ ] Pencil
- [ ] Piggy bank
- [ ] Robot
- [ ] Sailboat
- [ ] Snake
- [ ] Sunglasses
- [ ] Super-hero doll
- [ ] Tape measure
- [ ] Truck
- [ ] Unicorn
- [ ] Wreath
- [ ] Yellow star

Fee
Fi
Fo
Fun

The elves are hard at work making lots of wonderful gifts for Santa to deliver on Christmas Eve.

SEARCH FOR FEE, FI, FO, AND FUN AT SANTA'S WORKSHOP AND...

- [ ] Alien spaceship
- [ ] Airplanes (2)
- [ ] Astronaut
- [ ] Banana peel
- [ ] Barbell
- [ ] Bird
- [ ] Bottle
- [ ] Bowling ball
- [ ] Broom
- [ ] Candle
- [ ] Chimneys (3)
- [ ] Clock
- [ ] Fish
- [ ] Flower
- [ ] Frog
- [ ] Green feather
- [ ] Hockey stick
- [ ] Ice skate
- [ ] Juggler
- [ ] Magnifying glass
- [ ] Mallets (2)
- [ ] Moose head
- [ ] Mouse
- [ ] Nets (3)
- [ ] Race car
- [ ] Rocket ship
- [ ] Rocking chair
- [ ] Saddle
- [ ] Sailor hat
- [ ] Saw
- [ ] Screw
- [ ] Skateboard
- [ ] Sock
- [ ] Surfboard
- [ ] Tent
- [ ] Toy soldier
- [ ] TV antenna

Fee   Fi

Fo   Fun

The card makers are really busy this time of year.

SEARCH FOR FEE, FI, FO, AND FUN AT THE CHRISTMAS CARD FACTORY AND...

- ☐ Arrow
- ☐ Balloon
- ☐ Beach ball
- ☐ Bird
- ☐ Birdhouse
- ☐ Bone
- ☐ Broom
- ☐ Candle
- ☐ Cat
- ☐ Chair
- ☐ Cloud
- ☐ Curtains
- ☐ Dog
- ☐ Elephant
- ☐ Fake snow
- ☐ Feather
- ☐ Fish
- ☐ Flower
- ☐ Hammer
- ☐ Heart
- ☐ Ice skates
- ☐ Igloo
- ☐ Kite
- ☐ Lights (2)
- ☐ Models (4)
- ☐ Number 26
- ☐ Paint bucket
- ☐ Paintbrush
- ☐ Pencil
- ☐ Pizza
- ☐ Scarf
- ☐ Scissors
- ☐ Shovels (2)
- ☐ Star
- ☐ Turtle
- ☐ Wagon
- ☐ Wreath

Everybody loves to sing Christmas songs, especially the elves.

SEARCH FOR FEE, FI, FO, AND FUN AT THE CHRISTMAS CAROL SING-ALONG AND...

- [ ] Angel
- [ ] Balloons (5)
- [ ] Baseball cap
- [ ] Bells (2)
- [ ] Cactus
- [ ] Candy canes (2)
- [ ] Carrot
- [ ] Clothespin
- [ ] Deer
- [ ] Duck
- [ ] "Elfis"
- [ ] Elves wearing glasses (4)
- [ ] Elves with beards (2)
- [ ] Feather
- [ ] Flute
- [ ] Flying carpet
- [ ] Football helmet
- [ ] Horse
- [ ] Ice skates
- [ ] Jack-in-the-box
- [ ] Kettle drum
- [ ] Parrot
- [ ] Penguin
- [ ] Pillow
- [ ] Pizza
- [ ] Rabbits (2)
- [ ] School bag
- [ ] Singing tree
- [ ] Skier
- [ ] Torn gloves
- [ ] Tuba
- [ ] Watering can
- [ ] Wreaths (3)

Fee Fi Fo Fun

With a little teamwork, and a lot of elves, making wreaths is easy and fun to do.

SEARCH FOR FEE, FI, FO, AND FUN AT THE WREATH MAKERS AND...

- [ ] Balloon
- [ ] Bird
- [ ] Candle
- [ ] Candy cane
- [ ] Chair
- [ ] Christmas stockings (2)
- [ ] Crayon
- [ ] Crown
- [ ] Deer
- [ ] Doors
- [ ] Duck
- [ ] Falling star
- [ ] Fish
- [ ] Football
- [ ] Garden hose
- [ ] Ice skates
- [ ] Jack-in-the-box
- [ ] Jars of glue (3)
- [ ] Ladder
- [ ] Light bulbs (3)
- [ ] Mouse
- [ ] Oilcan
- [ ] Paintbrush
- [ ] Pencils (2)
- [ ] Picture frame
- [ ] Pizza
- [ ] Propeller
- [ ] Rake
- [ ] Rejected wreaths
- [ ] Roller skates
- [ ] Shovel
- [ ] Snake
- [ ] Television
- [ ] Top hat
- [ ] Turtle
- [ ] Umbrella
- [ ] Wagon
- [ ] Watering can

Fee	Fi
Fo	Fun

So many gifts... so little time... and they all have to be wrapped before Christmas Eve!

SEARCH FOR FEE, FI, FO, AND FUN AT THE GIFT WRAPPING DEPARTMENT AND...

- ☐ Airplane
- ☐ Arrows (2)
- ☐ Banana peel
- ☐ Baseball
- ☐ Basketball
- ☐ Books (3)
- ☐ Boots
- ☐ Candy canes (3)
- ☐ Carrot
- ☐ Christmas stockings (3)
- ☐ Computer
- ☐ Doll
- ☐ Drum
- ☐ Flower
- ☐ Footballs (2)
- ☐ Golf club
- ☐ Horn
- ☐ Kites (3)
- ☐ Lamp
- ☐ Lunch box
- ☐ Pencils (2)
- ☐ Piggy bank
- ☐ Rabbit
- ☐ Rocking horse
- ☐ Sailboat
- ☐ Scissors
- ☐ Snowmen (2)
- ☐ Star
- ☐ Tennis racket
- ☐ Tent
- ☐ Trampoline
- ☐ Tricycle
- ☐ Wrapped elf
- ☐ Wrapped gift

Fee Fi Fo Fun

'Tis the week before Christmas and at the North Pole not a creature is working, not even a mole. Why not? Because it's time for the elves' Christmas party!

SEARCH FOR FEE, FI, FO, AND FUN AT THE CHRISTMAS PARTY AND...

- [ ] Balloon
- [ ] Banana
- [ ] Bell
- [ ] Birds (2)
- [ ] Bows (4)
- [ ] Broom
- [ ] Clock
- [ ] Chef's hat
- [ ] Deer
- [ ] Dog
- [ ] Dracula
- [ ] Eyeglasses (2 pairs)
- [ ] Feather
- [ ] Fish
- [ ] Flowerpot
- [ ] Football helmet
- [ ] Guitar
- [ ] Igloo
- [ ] Jack-o'-lantern
- [ ] Loudspeaker
- [ ] Mama Claus
- [ ] Mouse
- [ ] Piano
- [ ] Pitcher
- [ ] Rocking chair
- [ ] Roller skates (2)
- [ ] Scrooge
- [ ] Seal
- [ ] Straw
- [ ] Top hats (2)
- [ ] Train engine
- [ ] Turtles (2)
- [ ] Umbrella

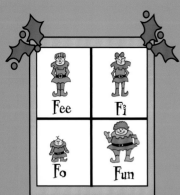

Fee Fi
Fo Fun

What a wonderful place to work. It looks like a delicious crop this year!

SEARCH FOR FEE, FI, FO, AND FUN AT THE CANDY CANE FARM AND...

- Airplane
- Ax
- Barn
- Barrel
- Baseball bat
- Birds (7)
- Broom
- Carrot
- Condo
- Crayon
- Crown
- Dog
- Elephant
- Evergreen tree
- Goat
- Goose
- Hammock
- Helicopter
- Hot dog
- Kangaroo
- Laundry
- Mailbox
- Mouse
- Pail
- Paint bucket
- Pencil
- Pig
- Polka-dotted cane
- Rabbit
- Reject basket
- Shovel
- Sled
- Snowball fight
- Straw hat
- Stripeless cane
- Tractor
- Wagon
- Watering can
- Windmill

Fee   Fi

Fo   Fun

The big night—
Christmas Eve— is
finally here! Everyone
is helping to pack the
sleigh, and Santa is
ready to go!

SEARCH FOR FEE,
FI, FO, AND FUN ON
CHRISTMAS EVE
AND...

- ☐ Apple
- ☐ Arrow
- ☐ Baseball
- ☐ Basket
- ☐ Bell
- ☐ Boots (2 pairs)
- ☐ Camera
- ☐ Candelabra
- ☐ Crayons (3)
- ☐ Drum
- ☐ Earmuffs
- ☐ Envelope
- ☐ Hockey stick
- ☐ Hoe
- ☐ Igloo
- ☐ Knitting needles
- ☐ Lollipop
- ☐ Picture frame
- ☐ Polka-dotted bow
- ☐ Propellers (2)
- ☐ Robot
- ☐ Sailboat
- ☐ Shovel
- ☐ Slide
- ☐ Stars (3)
- ☐ Stowaway
- ☐ Toaster
- ☐ Train engines (2)
- ☐ Umbrella
- ☐ Weather vane
- ☐ Wheelbarrow
- ☐ Wreath

Christmas greetings to you from Fee, Fi, Fo Fun, and their friends:

Freddie   Hector
Lisa   Laura
Susie   Santa
Frankie   Donald
Bunny Honey   Sam

SEARCH FOR SANTA'S HELPERS